A Lesson in Democracy

Comparing the EU and the US response to climate alarmism

Jeremy Nieboer

© The Bruges Group 2010
ISBN: 978-0-9564614-1-4

Published in March 2010 by
The Bruges Group, 227 Linen Hall, 162-168 Regent Street, London W1B 5TB
www.brugesgroup.com

Bruges Group publications are not intended to represent a corporate view of European and international developments. Contributions are chosen on the basis of their intellectual rigour and their ability to open up new avenues for debate.

The Author

Jeremy Nieboer, educated at Harrow School and Oxford, was called to the Bar in 1965 and admitted as a Solicitor in 1970. As a lawyer he specialises in corporate and commercial law. He worked with the Democracy Movement on opposition to EMU from 1997 – 2000 and gives regular talks to schools, including 6th forms, on EU issues organised by Civitas. Here he has often debated against speakers from the European Movement and Britain in Europe.

Jeremy Nieboer was the lead solicitor on the applications to the High Court and Court of Appeal for judicial review of the then Foreign Secretary's (Douglas Hurd) decision to ratify the Maastricht Treaty in 1993. He worked with Bill Cash MP, Lord Rees – Mogg, David Pannick QC and Martin Howe QC on the applications.

He is the author of *The Pros and Cons of Economic and Monetary Union*. Jeremy is on the Advisory Board of the European Foundation.

Table of Contents

Introduction 5

Where we are now 6

Is the science of Global Warming "certain"? 8

Is there a "consensus"? 17

Is the science settled? Conclusions 18

EU Policy Making and Global Warming 19

The EU Global Warming disaster 31

Mounting disquiet with the IPCC Process 32

Congress and Global Warming 34

The lesson to be learned 37

A LESSON IN DEMOCRACY
Comparing the EU and the US response to climate alarmism

Introduction

JEREMY NIEBOER, member of the Advisory Board of the European Foundation, reviews the present state of scientific opinion on the existence of any abnormal rise in temperature of the planet and the part, if any, that man made emissions of CO_2 can with confidence be said to have contributed to it. The four successive reports of the UN Intergovernmental Panel on Climate Change (IPCC) and the UK's own Stern Review suggest that climate change may well cause serious loss of global GDP by the end of this century with catastrophic tipping points likely to occur in 10 to 15 years time. However, examination of the evidence for these alarming conclusions indicates that they are riven with deep uncertainties. Not only is the body of scientific data as to the existence of global warming at best equivocal but there is also now clear and disturbing evidence of distortions and suppression of evidence by leading proponents of the case for global warming.

The paper examines how the EU has taken upon itself the role of championing the 'Fight against Climate Change', recognising that public alarm at the perceived perils mankind is facing could be turned to account by it to extend its powers and standing. In doing so it has ignored the serious doubts cast over the IPCC and Stern reports and has set targets for cuts in CO_2 emissions and for 'renewable' energy supply such that irreparable damage would be done to its subject economies were they to be fully implemented.

Mr Nieboer traces the progress of the EU's policy making in line with each of these reports and demonstrates that no process of democratic oversight or investigation has preceded its decisions. It has not initiated any independent research into or analysis of the scientific basis of the case for global warming or the proportionate response that should be made. It has simply relied without question on the flawed IPCC reports and the Stern Review. The paper contrasts this with the rigorous process of enquiry and research set on foot over 20 years by successive US Congressional Committees into every aspect of the subject and concludes that it is only to a robust and effective democracy that such decisions can safely be committed. This is the enduring lesson of the global warming alarm.

Where we are now

The failure of the United Nations global warming summit to secure a successor to Kyoto has been met with expressions of dismay and despair from world leaders. EU leaders called the failure a *'disaster'*. The best that could be achieved was a non binding accord between just 28 countries out of the 192 taking part as to climate change strategies and a general commitment to limiting global temperature increase to below 2° celsius. No measures were agreed which could mean this target could be met. Promises of US $100 billion a year to help developing nations from 2020 with US $30bn a year from 2010-12 did not come with any tangible proposals as to how this should be funded or expended. The EU, which had pledged to cut greenhouse gas emissions to 20 percent below 1990 levels by 2020 and to deepen that cut to 30 percent if agreement was reached at Copenhagen, has been left isolated.

Such a reaction is not however reflected in the evidence of popular concern. Shortly before the dismal closing scenes at Copenhagen an ICM survey in the UK for *The Daily Telegraph* revealed that 46% of those polled did not believe that mankind was mainly responsible for global temperature rises and that 39% did not believe that 'climate change' was caused by human activity. A survey conducted by Cardiff University showed that 4 out of 10 members of the public believed the evidence was questionable. In the USA a BBC World Service poll showed that only 45% of US citizens regard 'climate change' as really serious.

Yet such popular scepticsm is met with intolerance and even abuse by political leaders. The Prime Minister himself thought it appropriate to describe those who doubt that human activity contributes to global warming as *"flat earthers"* and *"anti – science"*.

As Copenhagen stumbled into contention and failure there appeared in the UK disturbing evidence of the contempt and fury of Mr Ed Milliband, Secretary of State of the department of Energy and Climate Change, and of the chief scientific adviser to that department at the public's reaction to a Government TV advertisement last November depicting a father reading a frightening bed time story on global warming. Following 785 complaints from members of the public this advertisement was investigated by Clearcast the advertising watchdog. The advertisement was described by Lord Lawson a *"mendacious"* in content and immoral in that its focus was to terrify young children. At the same time private research commissioned by Mr Milliband's department and leaked to Channel 4 News also revealed that those surveyed did not see climate change as having a serious impact in the UK.

In response to this Robert Watson, the chief scientific adviser to Mr Milliband's department, sent a furious letter to Clearcast asserting ... *"the incontrovertible nature of the science that underpins the campaign material"*. Mr Milliband himself told Channel 4 News that people who want to cast doubt on global warming as a serious problem for humanity *"...are the modern equivalent of the Flat Earth Society because the science is very clear about this. Climate change is real. It's happening. It's man-made. Frankly it's irresponsible to suggest that it isn't happening and it isn't man made"*

Such is the view of the responsible Government minister of the sincere doubts entertained by the public as to the existence, the causes and the likely impact of what has come to be called 'climate change'. It reveals a deep and disturbing arrogance in the political elite and its abiding contempt for the electorate with its presumption that popular democratic oversight and scrutiny has no place in determining the way forward for the people whose lives will be directly and profoundly affected by its decisions.

This paper will examine how both democratic oversight and also dependence on electoral goodwill may dislodge such overbearing assumptions and provide a rational and balanced judgment as to how humanity should regard the phenomenon of alarm at 'global warming' and assess what may be the most beneficial and proportionate means of dealing with any harm it may cause.

The proper stance for any government faced with apparent mounting concern at a seeming fundamental alteration in global temperature should be a rigorous and continuous examination of the evidence as to the existence, causes and probable consequences of this phenomenon. This would underpin a thorough assessment of the economic and political consequences of this change and of the options for dealing with it. As this paper will show no such stance has been adopted by the EU at any point in the widening debate on this issue or in the formulation of its policies.

No attempt is made in this paper to make a judgment on the competing contentions of the scientific world as to global warming. The only fact that can be unequivocally asserted is that the entire compass of this weighty matter - for the EU it is the *"defining challenge of our times"*[1] - is informed throughout by uncertainty.

Uncertainties extend to the separate questions of whether or not global warming is happening, whether it is likely to happen in the future, whether it is caused by

---

1   Connie Hedegaard, 2010 EU commissioner designate for climate action, address to European Parliament, 22 January 2010

human activity, what the net cost and damage (after crediting benefits and gain) to humanity may result and what may be the most beneficial policies to adopt in response.

Is the science of Global Warming "certain"?

It is necessary to pose some basic questions on 'Global Warming'. Does it exist? If so then what are its causes? What effects will it have? What damage will it inflict? What if anything should be done?

Is there 'global warming'?

It may seem impertinent to some that this question needs to be asked - so dominant is the assumption that *"climate change is real. It's happening"*. Of course there are and always will be variations in climate – what is of concern is whether there is a trend in warming of the planet that is in itself abnormal when looked at in the context of global temperature variations over adequate time scales.

Using the data of the Hadley Centre (working with the Climate Research Unit of the University of East Anglia – a strong proponent of global warming) the increase in global temperature was 0.4° from 1920 to 1940, with a cooling of -0.2° celsius from 1940 to 1976 and an increase of 0.5° celsius from 1976 – 1998. This represents an increase of approx 0.7° celsius for the whole of the 20th century.

However the official sources of temperature data show that there has been no global temperature rise overall since 1998. Lord Lawson[2] sets out in his very useful booklet[3] the average global temperatures published by the Hadley Centre. These show a fall from the 0.52° celsius excess over the 1961 – 1990 global average in 1998 to 0.31° celsius in 2008. The World Meteorological Organisation reported in December 2008 that global average temperature in 2008 was lower than the previous years of the decade[4].

The fall in global average temperature from January 2007 – January 2008 was the steepest since 1880.[5] By June 2009 temperatures for the month of June had

---

2   Nigel Lawson, Baron Lawson of Blaby, PC Chancellor of the Exchequer from June 1983 to October 1989, founder and chairman of the Global Warming Policy Foundation.

3   Nigel Lawson, *An Appeal to Reason – A Cool Look at Global Warming*

4   WMO Press Release No 835 16th December 2008

5   *Heaven and Earth* published by Quartet Books 2009, page 490. Author Professor Ian Plimer; School of Earth and Environmental Sciences University of Adelaide; Emeritus Professor of Earth Scientists at University of Melbourne. Where technical source material is referred to in these notes

fallen to exactly the average level over 30 years (the entire period for which there is satellite temperature data).

Predictions for temperature rise in the future are very difficult to sustain. The basis for predicted global temperature rise to 2100 set out in the UN's Intergovernmental Panel on Climate Change (IPCC) in its 2001 IPCC Report has now been discarded in circumstances which will be looked at later in this paper. The most recent IPCC Report (2007) confines its prediction to between 1.8° - 0.4° celsius. The IPCC models have pointed to the likelihood of greater warming in the lower atmosphere at the tropics. However satellite and radiosonde data show no mean warming in the tropics for the data period 1979 – 2004.[6]

It is not difficult to conclude that there exists a basic underlying uncertainty as to the existence of any upward trend in warming over the last 12 years.

Was human induced CO2 the cause of the global warming 1900 – 1998?
No one challenges the fact that from 1920 – 1998 global temperatures increased by approximately 0.7% as the world moved out of the two successive phases of what is known as the "Little Ice Age" (1350 AD – 1850 AD). What is uncertain is what has caused this increase.

In 1988 the accusing finger was pointed to the rise in CO2 concentration in the atmosphere. This has increased by more than 30% since measurements began in 1959. Such was the enthusiasm evoked by the coincidence of accelerating concentrations of CO2 and temperature rise that it was elevated to the status of definite causation. However there are great uncertainties as to the true cause of the temperature rise from 1976 to 1998.

The role of CO2 in the atmosphere needs to be set in its scientific context. CO2 makes up approximately 0.0385% of the gases in the atmosphere. CO2 concentration in the atmosphere is today only one ten thousandth greater than it was in 1750 AD[7]. Of the estimated 190 bn tonnes of CO2 taken into the atmosphere only 3.3% is down to human causes. After entering the atmosphere CO2 later becomes dissolved in the oceans[8]. Studies made by one of the promoters of the

---

and is not otherwise attributed it is taken from this work which is one of remarkable erudition and scholarship over the entire subject of climate change.

6   *Ibid*, pages 381/382

7   Keeling C.D. and Whorf T.P. 'Atmospheric carbon dioxide record from Mauna Loa', 2004. Plimer, *op. cit.*, page 490

8   Quay P.D. *et al..* 1992 Ocean uptake of fossil fuel CO2. Plimer, *op. cit.*, page 414

IPCC in 1988 show that the lifetime of CO_2 in the atmosphere is only 5.4 years and although a longer period is suggested in later IPCC reports no explanation is given for the discrepancy.[9]

It is accepted that at least two thirds of the greenhouse effect is accounted for by water vapour. Yet the actual effect of water vapour and cloud formation on climate is not fully understood. The IPCC, the best known international proponent of the case for global warming and its effects, itself acknowledged in its latest (2007) report that *"Cloud feedbacks remain the largest source of uncertainty"*.

It is also far from clear that increases in CO_2 concentrations produce a consequential proportionate increase in the greenhouse effect. There is support from eminent scientists that the efficiency of the greenhouse effect of CO_2 is not related to the amount of CO_2 in the atmosphere so that increasing CO_2 emissions by a factor of 3 or even more will not increase the trapping effect by more than a marginal amount.[10]

There are considerable historical anomalies as well. The cooling period from 1940 to 1976 is not readily explained – there was a rise in CO_2 emissions due to greatly increased industrial war time activity. Some say this is due to the dimming of the sun's radiation by sulphate aerosols emitted up to the late 1970s when this form of pollution was radically reduced. If this is so then how can there be a man made explanation of the warming from 1920 to 1940?

Furthermore CO_2 does not provide any explanation for the Mediaeval Warming from 950 AD to 1300 AD when temperatures were it appears higher than today, or the earlier warming in the Roman period between 200 BC and 540 AD, or the Minoan Warming from 1470 BC to 1300 BC.

On a greater geological scale during periods of severe planetary glaciation CO_2 levels in the atmosphere were up to 10 times greater than levels of today.[11]

It also seems possible and even probable that CO_2 emissions may be the result of, and not the cause of, planetary warming since COs is released from the oceans when temperatures rise; Antarctic ice cores appear to show this. The temperature rise from 1890 to 1940 preceded the increase in CO_2 in the last half of the 20th century.

9   Bolin B. and Eriksson E. 1959: Changes in the carbon dioxide content on the atmosphere due to fossil fuel combustion. Plimer, *op. cit.*, page 422

10 Plimer, *op. cit.*, page 374/375. Fred Hoyle: *Ice the Ultimate Human Catastrophe* 1981

11 Plimer *op. cit.* page 242

There is also no definite correlation between CO2 atmospheric increases and temperature changes – to take a most recent example the fall in global temperature from 1940 to 1976 was accompanied by CO2 rises whilst the fall in average global temperature in the period 1998 – 2009 was matched by a 25% increase in the burning of fossil fuels. However there is a close correlation between solar activity (sun spots and impact of cosmic rays on cloud formation) with evidence of falling solar energy likely to cause cooling to at least 2015 and possibly beyond.[12]

It will readily be seen from this brief summary that it is not at all certain that the temperature rise from 1976 – 1998 was caused by an increase in human emitted CO2 atmospheric concentrations. Certainly there is cause for ascribing uncertainty to the issue given that, whilst CO2 emissions from human activity have increased since 1998, temperature has remained at a standstill or has fallen.

What will happen to global temperature in the future?
If uncertainty attends any conclusion as to the causes of global warming and as to whether, if caused by the rise in CO2 concentrations, these are due to human activity, a far greater uncertainty shrouds predictions of computer models of what may happen in the future. Even Sir John Houghton, a battle hardened champion of the global warming case and former CEO of the UK Meteorological Office, has warned that *"you have to be very wary indeed of the answers you are getting"* when you put climate models and economic models together.

The forecasts of the Met Office for each of 2007, 2008 and 2009 were wrong despite the chronological proximity. In January 2007 it predicted that 2007 would be warmer than 1998 becoming *"the warmest year on record"* with global temperature increasing by 0.54° celsius, but temperatures fell drastically for the coldest year since 1995. It predicted that 2008 would be *"one of the top ten warmest years ever recorded"* – it proved to be one of the coldest of the last 50 years with Antarctic sea ice cover at its highest recorded March level with Arctic sea ice greatly increased. The Met Office then forecast that 2009 would be *"one the five warmest years on record"* but later had to acknowledge that the winter was the coldest for 13 years.

If such forecasts are so gravely in error, suggesting at the least a prevailing uncertainty, how can it reasonably be asserted that the *"science is clear"*?

It is important to retain a sense of proportion about all this. The latest IPCC's projection of temperature rise over this century to 2100 varies from 1.8° celsius for its lowest emissions estimate to 4° celsius for its highest emissions estimate

---

12   *Ibid*, page 242

– an average of 2.9° celsius. This does not take account of the standstill of global temperature since 1998. Such an increase over the 100 years to 2010 is the equivalent of 0.029° each year.

To put it in context, it should be remembered that during the period since the so called Maunder Minimum from 1645 to 1715 global temperature has risen by a naturally occurring 0.5° Celsius per 100 years but during the major part of which industrialisation had no influence. Yet global temperature is approximately 3° celsius lower than during the Mediaeval and Roman Warmings[13].

If there is such uncertainty in predictions of the temperature of the planet in the years to come the scope for error becomes vastly extended when assessing what impact a rise in global temperature may have upon mankind. The IPCC itself makes it clear in its 2001 Report that *"In climate research and modelling, we should recognise that we are dealing with a complex non-linear chaotic system and therefore that the long term prediction of future climate states is not possible."*

It is necessary to look briefly at each of the impacts predicted by the IPCC to establish if they can be determined with sufficient certainty to found a rational and beneficial response for mankind.

What damage is likely to be caused?
What are the perils that the IPCC detect when it looks into future? What will be the damage caused by global warming and what costs will result from the changes wrought by it?

A summary of how the IPCC views the likely impact of global warming is set out in Lord Lawson's booklet *An Appeal to Reason: A Cool Look at Global Warming*[14]. In short the IPCC in its latest 2007 report expects that there will adverse impacts on water resources, plant and animal extinctions, food supply, land erosion and submersion and health.

Water supplies
Water supplies have not been affected by the 0.7° celsius warming in the 20th century. Whilst the water cycle is a dominant influence on climate there is no necessary correlation between CO2 levels and rainfall and river flow. What is known is that there is a close correlation of the hydro meteorological process and sunspot

---

13   Petit J.R. *et al.*. Climate and atmospheric history of the past 420,000 years from the Vostok ice core Antarctica, 1999. Plimer, *op. cit.*, page 490

14   Nigel Lawson, *An Appeal to Reason – A Cool Look at Global Warming*

activity[15]. Flood defence is well known to mankind. Water shortages, if they occur at all may be met by making supplies more efficient and less wasteful with recourse to desalination plants only if necessary. Population pressures will dictate action of this kind.

There is also much doubt as to possible increased drought. The IPCC 2001 report asserts that *"increased continental drying and associated risk of drought is likely..."* Yet the evidence suggests that droughts in central USA have become shorter, less frequent and less severe and cover a smaller area in the 20th century and that deserts are not expanding and may be contracting in Africa[16]. It appears now that deserts in China are retreating by 7,500 sq kilometres a year.[17]

Extinctions
IPCC predictions are that a 0.8° celsius temperature rise over 50 years could result in extinction of 20% of species. This is a conclusion based on one species – the golden toad – which lost its only habitat in the Monteverde (Costa Rica) cloud forest and became extinct. This was ascribed to global warming. However the authors of the relevant study on which these predictions are based made it clear that lowland deforestation may well have been the cause.

Whatever the strength of emotions engendered by the thought of irretrievable loss of plants and animals it must be remembered that 99.9% of all species that have ever existed on our planet are now extinct. The conclusions of leading scientists in this field[18] on the extent of extinction in the last 2.5 million years are that a surprisingly low number of the planet's plant and animal species have become extinct. This period encompassed times of great variations of climate not least the recent (in geological terms) Minoan, Roman and Mediaeval Warmings. No mass extinctions occurred in these periods. Geology shows that in times of global warming life diversifies and increases.

Food shortages
Food shortages have been, and remain in many parts of the world, a terror for mankind. The IPCC acknowledges that food production will in fact increase

---

15   Alexander W. Locally-developed climate model verified, 2007. Plimer, *op. cit.*, pages 360/361

16   Herrmann S. *et al..* Recent trends in vegetation dynamics in the African Sahel and their relationship to climate, 2005. Plimer, *op. cit.*, page 204

17   Plimer, *op. cit.*, page 205

18   Botkin D.B. Forecasting the effects of global warming on biodiversity and Wall Street Journal 17th October 2001 Global Warming Delusions.

(ignoring for this purpose improved technology and adaptation) with a temperature rise of up to 3° celsius – slightly more than the mean IPCC predicted increase - but that it will decrease at higher levels.

Warming brings into agriculture land that could not be tilled and there is clear evidence of food surpluses in the Roman and Mediaeval Warmings supporting rises in populations. The Doomsday book shows grapes grown in places which could not sustain them even now. CO_2 increases are entirely beneficial to plant life. At 200 parts per million (ppmv) plant growth almost ceases whilst agricultural hothouses are forced up to 1000 ppmv to create high yields and faster growth. In the most recent warming period of 900AD to 1300AD there is abundant evidence that agriculture thrived in locations which could not today sustain it[19] with vineyards in Germany 700ft higher than today's highest level at an indicated temperature up to 1.7° higher than now.[20]

The most that can be said about the predictions of the IPCC itself as to the extent of likely global warming to 2100 is that, if true, they mean that this will not be the cause of any fall in food production.

Land inundation
The spectre of land submersion and global inundation has long haunted mankind. The movement on the line of the Anatolian Fault some 7,500 years ago caused the collapse and dispersal of the rock barrier protecting the land now forming the basin of the Black Sea from the Sea of Marmara resulting in the catastrophic inundation which formed it in only 2 years – a possible explanation of the origin of the Biblical Flood. However, the alarm – even terror - which forecasts of catastrophic inundations may have stimulated should not be allowed to obscure the fact that sea level changes are not showing any abnormal trends.

Sea levels changes are very difficult to determine. Satellite measurements point to a rise in sea levels in the 20th century of 2.4 mm per year but with approx 1.5mm for the last half of the century. However there is respected expert opinion that the maximum rise from 1850 – 1940 was no greater than 1.1mm.[21] GPS data show

19   Lacey R. *et al.*. The year 1000: *What life was like at the turn of the First Millenium*, 1999. . Plimer, *op. cit.* page 64

20   Plimer, *op. cit.*, pages 64 and 248

21   Nils-Axel Morner. Head of Paleogeophysics and Geodynamics at Stockholm University. Past President (1999 – 2003) INQUA Commission on Sea Level Changes and Coastal Evolution and leader of the Maldives Sea Level Project. EIR News Service, Inc. interview 22nd June 2007

global sea levels rising at only 0.84mm in the 6 years to 2007 although other data point to slightly higher increases.[22]

Nor is the process constant or global. During the warming period from 1920 to 1940 sea level rises ceased[23]. There are very wide variations locally. Many surface parts of the planet are sinking whilst others (for example coral founded islands) are rising or maintaining a constant level. In the central Pacific (including Tuvalu), the latest technology used by Flinders University of South Australia showed that sea levels were static over the entire 10 year period of study from 1993. GPS data show actual falls[24] in levels in this region.

The unreliability of any predicted rise in sea level rise is reflected in the variation in the IPCC forecasts over the last 17 years. The 1990 IPCC Report predicted sea level rises by 2100 of 66cm (26") revising it in 1996 to 49cm (19") and again in 2001 to a mean (20-88cm) of 54 cm (21") and again in 2007 to a mean of 38.5 cm (15") with variable margins of 18 – 59 cm (7" – 23"). However the IPCC values have been severely criticised by one its experts as being *"completely misleading and false"*.[25] There is cogent evidence from satellite telemetry data which shows that there has been almost no change over the last 10 years[26] and that sea level rise to 2100 will only be +10 or -10 cm with a maximum of 5cm.[27]

It is surely clear from all this that no certainty can be attached to any model or other predicted sea level increases due to human produced CO_2 in the next 100 years on such a scale as to warrant global action to mitigate its consequences.

Health problems
The IPCC focus on health in its latest Report (2007) is largely concerned with the transmission of malaria and other diseases from the tropics to Europe and North America. It is as well to remember that periods of warming have historically been periods of great increases in the wellbeing of mankind. This is very evident in the Minoan, Roman and Mediaeval Warmings. Malaria is a disease of poverty, not of climate. It was endemic in England in the 17th century at a time of the very cold

---

22   Plimer, *op. cit.*, page 311

23   Plimer, *op. cit.*, page 300

24   Cabanes C. *et al.*. 2001 Sea level rise during the past 40 years determined from satellite and in situ observations.

25   Plimer, *op. cit.*, pages 64 and 248

26   Nils-Axel Morner 2004 Estimating future sea level changes from past records.

27   Plimer, *op. cit.*, pages 64 and 248

conditions of the Little Ice Age and has been recorded as far north as Inverness. The decline in malaria occurred after the Little Ice Age had ceased and was the result of land drainage, increased use of mechanisation and the wide distribution of quinine.

The general assertion that over then next 50 or 100 years there will be global health problems due to increased atmospheric CO2 has no cogent scientific basis. CO2 levels in the mid 19th century were over 425 parts per million (at present 385 ppmv) and no global health problems have been ascribed to this fact.[28]

What will such damage cost if not prevented or mitigated?
The IPCC attempts a prediction as to the likely net cost of the damage that a warmer climate will inflict. Here the exercise almost entirely loses any utility. To attempt it at all it is necessary to take a figure from the widely varied predicted temperature increases postulated at various times by the IPCC. Since it is the most recent the predicted increase in the 2007 report should be treated as the basis of this enquiry. This proposed an increase by 2100 of 1.8° and 4° celsius. The IPCC estimate that, taking the 4° celsius rise in temperature, the cost measured as a percentage of global GDP would be between 1% and 5% and with greater loss for the developing world

What does this mean in reality?
Lord Lawson approaches this by assuming a supposed loss of as much as 10% of GDP for the developing world, to allow for the worse position it occupies, and a 3% loss for the developed world. He then applies the most pessimistic of the IPCC suppositions of a 3.4% rise in global temperature taken with the lowest IPCC predicted rise in living standards and the highest predicted growth of world population to 15bn by 2100 – nearly 65% higher than the UN's median projection. Even on this basis the rise in living standards would be 1% per year in the developed world and 2.3% in the developing world - ignoring global warming.

Applying the IPCC's prediction of GDP global warming cost, Lord Lawson demonstrates that by 2100 the developing world's inhabitants would be 2.6 times better off than today instead of 2.7 times. For the developed world the comparable figures are 8.5 times better off to 9.5 times.

If this is anything approaching a fair assessment of the IPCC's own predictions can it really be contended that there is certainty that drastic action must now be

---

28 Beck E.G. 2007 180 years of atmospheric CO2 gas analysis by chemical methods. Plimer, *op. cit.*, page 203

taken to defend mankind against the imagined peril that is to engulf the planet and mankind?

What is the cost of doing anything meaningful about global warming?
It will be seen that to get to this question assumptions have to be made at each stage as to the existence, causes and cost and damage of global warming. All of these factors are attended by great uncertainty.

What then can be said as to the cost of mitigating the damage global warming may inflict? The IPCC addresses this in its 2007 report. In the draft of the Summary for Policy Makers this was put at a cost, as a percentage of global yearly 2050 GDP, of between 1% - 5% to achieve cuts in CO2 to stabilise atmospheric concentrations at 550 ppmv by 2050. This would mean that a cost of 1% – 5% of GDP would be incurred to prevent a cost in global GDP also of 1% – 5%.

However the consequences of this absurdity were modified in the full final report to a lower target of 535 ppmv by 2050 with cost margins of nil% to 4% of 2050 GDP. Even on this revised basis the IPCC Report concluded that the *"costs and benefits of mitigation ...are broadly comparable in magnitude"* even if mitigation was possible in the absence of a binding global agreement.

Even Mike Hulme, the Professor of Climate Change at East Anglia University, a strong proponent of the need to address global warming and a contributor to the IPCC, has now cast doubt on the desirability of taking any form of drastic action urging that the better course is for humanity to accommodate to such climate change as may occur.

Is there a "consensus"?

Is it the case that there is an overwhelming body of scientific opinion that man made global warming is a serious threat to the wellbeing of mankind?

Again there can be little confidence that the IPCC represents a 'consensus' of scientific opinion. It is now clear that the key elements of the text of the IPCC Reports Summary for Policy Makers are prepared by a very limited number of authors indeed — far fewer than the increasingly numerous number of scientists who have published statements of deep unease as to the methods and conclusions of the IPCC. In 1996 the UN Climate Change Bulletin reported that 48% of 400 US and Canadian scientists had no faith in the IPCC climate models. A 1997 survey of US State Climatologists in 1997 found that 90% agreed that *"scientific evidence indicates variations in global temperature are likely to be naturally occurring and cyclical over very long periods of time"*. Yet this was in the run up to Kyoto and very soon after the second of the IPCC Reports with its alarmist predictions of human induced global warming.

The so called Oregon Petition (1999/2001 re-circulated 2007/8) urging the US Congress to reject the Kyoto Protocol and any similar mitigation of climate change was signed by 32,000 scientists and involved not just an online affirmation of support but the completing of a printed form and posting it to the Oregon Institute for Science and Medicine. The petition asserted *"that there is no convincing scientific evidence the human released... greenhouse gasses is causing or will, in the foreseeable future, cause catastrophic heating of the Earth's atmosphere and disruption of the Earth's climate"*.

A US Congressional Report in 2007 (Senate Environment and Public Works Committee Minority Report) listed more than 400 academic scientists world wide – many actual participants in the IPCC process – who expressed strong dissent from any 'consensus view' on global warming. This report has now been updated to March 2009 and has been subscribed by more than 700 dissenting scientists whose names, experience and qualifications together with a resumé of the grounds on which they base their dissent have been published and are available on the internet.

Even if science were to be validated by consensus – a concept that all scientific method finds repugnant – it cannot be said that a consensus of an overwhelming majority exists.

Is the science settled? Conclusions

In this paper it is not possible to do more than review the key assertions of the IPCC as to the existence, causes and effects of the supposed global warming and examine the extent to which they may fairly described as derived from science that is "certain" and *"incontrovertible"*.

Such an adamant conclusion cannot be justified, much less that those who doubt it be regarded as *"anti-science"* or *"irresponsible"* or *"flat earthers"*. Given the extent of uncertainty as to the basic tenets of the belief in global warming and in the terrors it holds for mankind such comments appear as the cries of members of a cult whose dogma and superstitions are brought into question and who seek to suppress all rational discussion or enquiry.

For the purposes of this paper it is enough to conclude that sufficient doubt exists as to the existence and the causes of supposed global warming, the damage resulting from it, the costs it will inflict on mankind and the cost of mitigating it to justify a thorough and informed analysis of each of these key issues before we are committed to costs and measures that will greatly increase the burden of taxes falling on industry, commerce and all of us individually and severely undermine our competitive position in the global economy.

EU Policy Making and Global Warming

How then have those who govern us approached this challenge? The European Union has been and remains the most important and vociferous global participant in the "fight against climate change". For the EU this remains *"the defining challenge of our times"*[29]. If this is the case it is legitimate to ask what is the serious and ongoing analysis of these key issues that underwrites such statements and which go to the foundation of any tenable policy on global warming that it has put in hand.

To help with this enquiry it is appropriate to review the legal basis on which the EU has entrenched its authority over matters concerning the environment.

The EU and the legal framework

The Single European Act (1986) first established competence of the EU in environmental matters. The EU has a 'shared competence' in the area of environment (Lisbon Treaty Article 4.2) This confers on the EU an overriding competence to legislate and adopt legally binding acts if it decides to do so and Member States have competence only to the extent that the EU has not exercised competence or has decided to cease doing so. Qualified majority voting on environmental issues was introduced by the Treaty of Amsterdam (1997).

Article 191 of Lisbon (formerly Article 174 of 1992 Maastricht Treaty) enshrines the EU's powers and competence but also extends the EU's competence expressly to *"combating climate change"*. The EU is bound under this Article – and has been bound at all material times since the emergence of the clamour as to global warming – to take account of four key factors in preparing its policy. It is worth enumerating these since they bear directly on the question of how the EU has dealt with global warming.

In preparing its policy on the environment the EU is bound to take account of:

---

29   Connie Hedegaard, 2010 EU commissioner designate for climate action, address to European Parliament, 22nd January 2010

1. Available scientific and technical data;
2. Environmental conditions in the various regions of the EU;
3. The potential benefits and costs of action or lack of action; and
4. The economic...development of the EU as a whole and the balanced development of its regions.

Before departing from Lisbon it is as well to recall that under Article 17 that treaty the Commission is required to be "completely independent" and its members are prohibited from seeking or taking instructions from any government or other institution, body, office or entity.

Since the emergence of the concern as to possible global warming the EU has assumed and has maintained its posture in the role of leading the world in the "fight against climate change". This is the fanfare that has preceded any pronouncement on the subject. It is instructive to trace the steps the EU has taken along the road laid out by the IPCC to see if it has abided by its own criteria of policy making.

1990 IPCC Report: "EU Community Strategy"
1990 saw the publication of the first IPCC report. This had a very cautious approach to the concern as to human CO_2 emissions as a contributor or cause of global warming. Even the Summary for Policy Makers – usually more dramatic in its potted conclusions than the full reports – warned that it would not be possible to reach an unequivocal view for ten years or more. The report itself stated that *"...we do not understand the reasons for....past warming events... [and] it is not yet possible to attribute a specific proportion of the recent smaller warming to an increase of greenhouse gases".*

There was wide concern at the use of computer modelling to arrive at the evidence underpinning the IPCC case. These methods took no account of water vapour and the negative feed back effect of clouds. Professor Lindzen (Professor of Meteorology at the Massachusetts Institute of Technology) expressed great concern at the single focus on CO_2 in the modelling and the failure to explain the significant variations in temperature in the 20th century concluding that the findings were *"disturbingly arbitrary"*[30].

---

30   Lindzen R. Global warming: the origin and nature of the alleged scientific consensus: OPEC seminar on the environment April 1992. Dr Richard Lindzen, Professor of Meteorology at the Massachusetts Institute of Technology, has published more than 200 books and scientific papers. He was a lead author of Chapter 7, 'Physical Climate Processes and Feedbacks,' of the 2001 IPCC Third Assessment Report on climate change

However none of this concern disturbed or impeded the EU. It moved without demur in October 1991 to publish its "Community Strategy to limit Carbon Dioxide Emissions" asserting that the IPCC 1990 report represented for the first time a consensus of world wide scientific opinion on the impact of climate change. As if excited by the opportunity to promote, in new and wider fields, its unique 'supranational' political status it demanded immediate action proclaiming that a decision to stabilise CO2 emissions was the first important step.

The Commission proposed that renewable energy should be actively promoted (primarily by wind power but excluding large hydro electric schemes). Regulations were to be imposed to limit CO2 emissions by industrial plants, vehicles and household fittings with a transfer from private to collective transport. The crowning piece of this edifice of measures was to be the imposition of a heavy "carbon tax".

Further empowered by the 1992 Maastricht Treaty the Commission introduced its "Proposal for a Council Directive Introducing a Tax on Carbon Dioxide Emissions and Energy".

Above all, the EU was to set a moral example to the world on climate change and it is this that has been its driving force. No independent research or investigation, testimony or hearings were initiated or sought by the EU to underwrite such major policy initiatives and the call for such major changes. Dr Roger Revelle, the chief scientific adviser to Al Gore, counselled in 1991 *"Look before you leap"*[31] urging that *"if we take any action it should be an action that we can justify completely without global warming".* This was never to be a guiding precept for the EU.

The requirement for "taking account of all available scientific and technical data" was deemed to be wholly fulfilled by an unquestioning acceptance as settled science of the tentative and uncertain conclusions of the IPCC report. The potential benefits and costs of action, or lack of action, were not examined in any thorough and comprehensive assessment of all relevant factors and options.

All that can be said is that if the IPCC project was itself partly politically inspired, the actions of the EU following the publication of the 1990 report made it disturbingly evident that, for the Commission, climate change was a political project masked as an environmental concern. In this is reflected the same process of delusion that the Commission sought to foster as to Economic and Monetary Union being an essentially commercial and economic advance and the fundamental concealment of the true foundation of the entire EU project itself.

---

31   Revelle R. *et al.. What to do about greenhouse warming: look before you leap*, 1991.

1996 IPCC Report: EU limits global warming to 2°: 8% emissions cuts

In 1996 the IPCC published its second report. This paved the way for the limitations on greenhouse gasses prescribed at Kyoto two years later which itself was the basis for even more severe reductions adopted by the EU. It therefore deserves study.

The 1996 report deepened concern as to global warming by its much more definite assertion in the Summary for Policy Makers that *"the balance of evidence suggests that there is a discernible human influence on global climate"*. However protests of scientific contributors to the main body of the report (of which this statement purported to be a summary) revealed that key passages in the text had been deleted after having been agreed by the examining scientists. These text passages included the statement *"None of the studies cited above has shown clear evidence that we can attribute the observed changes to the specific causes on increases in greenhouse gas"* and that *"no study to date has positively attributed all or part [of the climate change observed] to [human] causes"*. A Wall Street Journal editorial "Cover-up in the Greenhouse" ensured that this flaw was brought to world wide attention.

Not disturbed at all by the uncertainties which all this suggested, the EU, on the basis of this report, set out a policy objective on 25 June 1996 (Council Meeting Luxembourg) stating that it *"believes that global average temperature should not exceed 2 degrees above the pre-industrial level and that therefore concentration levels lower than 550 ppmv should guide global and reduction efforts"*. It is clear (see for example EU Commission Staff Working Paper on Winning the Battle against Climate Change 2 February 2005) that its conclusions were entirely based on the IPCC 1996 report. No attempt was made to verify, corroborate or investigate independently the conclusions of the report or the serious concerns expressed as to its validity.

The momentum to Kyoto was however not in the least arrested by these revelations. Borne forward by the IPCC report and appeals from Vice-President Gore and the UN Secretary General the signatory countries (excluding India and China) agreed to reduce emissions of greenhouse gasses by 2008 – 2010 to a level of 5.2% of 1990 levels – a true reduction of 29% by 2010 due to the increase in emissions since 1990. Kyoto also introduced into the international arena the concept of "emissions trading" under which carbon credits could be acquired by emitters who exceed the prescribed limits from those who had kept within them. To enable this to be administered there would now be a 'Clean Development Mechanism' administered by the UN Framework Convention on Climate Change.

Kyoto did not attempt to cost the impact of these measures to the affected economies. However in the US a figure of $716 bn was estimated to be the cost to its economy for the initial stage of emission reductions [32]. Nor were the benefits quantified to any degree. It was widely accepted that Kyoto could do no more than reduce global temperature by 0.05° even if 100% successful[33]. An adviser to Vice President Gore predicted that if fully implemented Kyoto would delay global warming by just 6 years[34]. The fundamental and continuing flaw was of course the fact that China (then 2nd largest emissions) and India (4th largest emissions) would not accept such restrictions.

The withdrawal of the US government's signature and its refusal to ratify the Kyoto Protocol left the EU with an open field of battle on which it could alone raise the standard in its fight against climate change. There were no democratic concerns that might give it pause since the Commission was and remains entirely isolated from the peoples it governs and immune to any infection of popular concern or sentiment. No manifesto was required to be placed before the citizens of its Member States for their judgment and electoral approval.

EU 2000 European Climate Change Programme:
10% of energy from renewables
Fortified by this fact the EU set targets for reductions in greenhouse gas emissions even more severe than Kyoto. Thus its Member States were committed to a reduction of 8% in emissions below 1990 levels for 2008/2010 – a vast reduction given the increase since 1990. It then moved to launch its 2000 European Climate Change Programme committing to a Kyoto target of 10% of all EU energy being provided from 'renewable' sources. It further committed itself to a directive setting an indicative target that by 2010 21.1% of electricity should be derived from renewables and requiring that Member States ensure that the origin of electricity produced from renewable resources could be guaranteed as such.

However no independent and professional analysis of the benefits and the costs of such measures was obtained to support them. The cost would of course result largely from the serious impact these measure would have on the generation of electricity from fossil fuels representing approximately 40% of all CO2 emissions.

---

32   Nordhaus W.D. *et al.. Requiem for Kyoto: An Economic Analysis of the Kyoto Protocol*, 1999. Professor of Economics; Cowles Foundation, Yale University, New Haven

33   Parry M. *Adapting to the inevitable*, 1998

34   Wigley A.M.T, *The Kyoto Protocol CO2, CH4 and Climate Implications*, 1998

In particular, no analysis of the costs and benefits of nuclear power, as the obvious alternative energy source, preceded these measures nor any serious review of the cost and effectiveness of the favoured alternative of wind power. The cost of per kilowatt of electricity generated by an onshore wind turbine, allowing for the necessary stand-by power plant to cover periods when no wind power is being generated, was reliably estimated to be 5.4p per kilowatt in 2004 for onshore windmills with coal sourced generation coming in at 2.5p, nuclear at 2.3p and gas at 2.2p.[35] Offshore windmills would cost 7.2p per kilowatt - a very severe cost increase for the consumer and for industry even without the imposition of carbon taxes to promote its policy on the use of renewables.[36]

Nor would wind power be capable of meeting the required minimum levels of electricity generation. As anyone who has flown over Denmark can attest, wind turbines have sprung up there as it has attempted to meet EU targets. However by 2004 wind turbines, which were supposed to produce 20% of electricity generation actually, only provided 6% of all electricity used with an average over the last 5 years of only 9.7%. The flaw is that the windmills require costly stand by power generation to compensate for the periods when wind is not powering the turbines.

When the electorates of Member States come fully to realise the cost penalties that flow from imposing measures of this kind and witness the futility of policies on wind power to meet these targets there must in time be serious electoral consequences for any government charged with imposing them. However such considerations do not weigh with the Commission whose members do not have to justify their policies in any democratic process nor face eviction from office by any electorate for their folly.

2001 IPCC Report: EU "Winning the Battle Against Climate Change"
A high point of alarm was created by the IPCC 2001 Report which predicted that in this century global temperatures would leap by 5.8° with astonishing accelerations which were already occurring. These were very grave predictions which caused world wide concern and fear.

However the 2001 Report has now been so discredited that it is astonishing that any public body or authority could conceivably rely on, let alone base a transformation of society, upon its findings. Yet this is the report on which the EU relied on to justify its target of keeping global temperature increase to 2° compared to pre-industrial

---

35   *The Cost of Generating Electricity*, 2004. Royal Academy of Engineering

36   Wigley A.M.T, *The Kyoto Protocol CO2, CH4 and Climate Implications*, 1998

levels and its climate change strategies (see Commission Communication COM (2005) 09.02.2005; Commission Staff Working Paper 09.02.2005 and "Winning the Battle Against Climate Change" 06.04.2005).

The 2001 Report depended in large measure for its alarming conclusion as to global temperature rise on a diagram or graph depicting a temperature trend. The graph purported to show temperature incidence over the last 1000 years and predicted temperature change. Its author was a Michael Mann of the University of Massachusetts. This graph had two features. It did not show the Mediaeval Warming Period from 950 AD – 1300 AD or the Little Ice Age from, 1450 – 1850 AD but only a fairly level average – these earlier periods were simply not there. It also, most alarmingly, showed a veritable explosion in global temperature from the last quarter of the 20th century so severe that it appears like the upward line of the base of a hockey stick. This was the key evidence justifying the IPCC predicted temperature increases of up to 5.8° Celsius higher - by 2.3° celsius - than its 1996 prediction.

The computer modelling that justified exclusion of the earlier known temperature variations in the Mediaeval Warming Period or the Little Ice Age and the alarming hike at the end of the 20th century, and beyond, caused these findings to be examined by statistical and computer modelling experts. Two US congressional committees also initiated research and reports into the Mann analysis. The 2003 reports of S McIntyre and R McKitrick showed that the entire computer modelling was based on a false "principal component analysis" that identified a hockey stick shape as the dominant pattern whatever data were fed in. The computer programme would *"pull out spurious hockey stick shapes from lists of trendless random numbers"*. Or as Churchill had it "Garbage in – Garbage out".

Such a fundamental falsehood would have been readily discovered on any proper and careful peer review of the Mann findings before they were embraced by the IPCC.

A further flaw revealed in the Mann graph was that Mann depended on tree ring evidence of high altitude bristlecone pines in California which had been collected for a 1993 report on the effect of CO_2 on growth at altitude but which, as the report made clear, could not be explained by temperature changes. It was found that as soon as the bristlecone pine data were removed the hockey stick effect also disappeared. More disturbing still, it was shown from his working papers that Mann knew that this would happen.

None of this altered the position of the EU in any way at all. It must be assumed that the Commission was aware of the studies of S McIntyre and R McKitrick and of the Congressional hearings in 2005/6 on the 2001 IPCC report which found the graph to be fundamentally flawed. If so, is it really an overstatement to assert that for the EU to rely on this report once it had become clear that it was indeed fundamentally flawed was unpardonable?

Certainly by March 2006 when the US National Research Council reported to the House of Representatives Science Committee on the Mann graph it was clear that there were, putting it charitably, fundamental uncertainties. Yet in March 2007 the EU proclaimed its 20:20:20 strategy following it up with its Green Paper *Adapting to Climate Change in Europe* in June 2007 and *Combating Climate Change – the EU Leads the Way* in September 2007.

EU's 20 20 by 2020 strategy; 10% of transport fuels from renewables
By the beginning of 2007 the EU was ready to make its next lunge to secure further powers with which to "fight climate change". At the March 2007 EU Council meeting it announced that by 2020 at least 20% of energy in the EU must be generated from renewable energy sources. It further required that at least 10% of all fuel used for transport be "biofuels" (derived from crops). In addition the EU set a reduction of at least 20% in greenhouse gases by 2020, rising to 30% if an adequate international agreement on emissions reductions was put in place – together the '20:20:20 strategy'. On top of all this it called for global emission reductions of up to 50% of 1990 levels by 2050. The Commission acknowledged that the issue of climate change was now "at the heart of the EU's political programme" and involved the *"transformation of the European economy requiring a major political, social, and economic effort"*.[37]

By this time the costs of meeting the EU targets was causing deep concern amongst those EU Member States in which serious enquiry was being made as to whether they were even remotely achievable and the damage on their economies that they would inflict – not least by migration of industrial concerns beyond the territorial grasp of the EU. The Chief Executive of ThyssenKrupps estimated that these measures would result in a loss in the Federal Republic of up to 500,000 jobs whilst in the UK the Taxpayers Alliance reported in September 2007 that 'green taxes' in the UK were running at £2.9 bn a year. The Carbon Trust estimated that at £2bn for each gigawatt of generating capacity the cost of installing the 7,000 giant

---

37   Communication from the Commission to the European Parliament – 20 20 by 2020 –Europe's climate change opportunity. COM (2008) 13 final. 23.01.2008

windmills needed to meet the 20:20:20 target would be approaching £66bn with costs of connection to the National Grid a further addition to the 'green' bill.

Worse still, since wind is intermittent and electricity cannot be stored in volume, the nominal capacity of the windmills is no guide to actual generation. Actual generation is less than one third (33%) of nominal capacity, requiring back up power stations to supply the shortfall. In Germany all its 18,000 windmills in 2006 could actually produced no greater than what it would take one coal-fired power station to generate. The Danish experience is that the cost per ton of CO2 saved by use of wind power is €87 as against the cost of CO2 saving by building insulation of no more than €20 per ton. Any fair examination of wind power reveals that the entire 20:20:20 project on which it is based is clearly unaffordable and impossible to realise.

2006 Stern Review

Such inconvenient facts did not appear to raise any concerns at the Commission. It may be that by 2007 it realised that IPCC 2001 was perhaps not entirely flawless. However it had a new armourer in its war on climate change – the Stern Review. This came upon the scene of battle in October 2006. The Stern Review is the additional foundation on which the EU has constructed its edifice of 20:20:20. It is expressly relied on in all the key EU policy documents from the moment that it appeared including the Green Paper *"Adapting to Climate Change in Europe"* June 2007, the Communication of Commission *"Europe's Climate Change Opportunity"* COM/2008/final 23rd January 2008 and the White Paper "Adapting to Climate Change: Towards a European framework for action" published on 1st April 2009 – an appropriate date perhaps.

The Review set out to provide the UK Prime Minister and Chancellor of the Exchequer with an assessment of the nature of the economic challenges of climate change and how they could be met, both in the UK and globally. It was published on 30th October 2006 its author being Lord Stern, the then Head of the Government Economic Service and former World Bank Chief Economist.

If the 2001 IPCC report attracted much criticism the Stern Review has attracted ridicule. It did not initiate independent enquiries or investigations into the causes and effects of climate change but relied on selected reports to justify apocalyptic findings. It asserted that scientific evidence for global warming caused by human emitted greenhouse gasses was *"overwhelming"* ignoring altogether the findings of the Congressional Committee reports and hearings condemning the hockey stick graph which had just been concluded. Amongst its more extravagant predictions was that up to 40% of the planet's species could become extinct with 100,000,000 people driven from their homes by flooding. Even more startling was the claim that the damage caused by global warming would inflict a loss in global GDP of at least 5% *"each year now and forever"*.

Dr Richard S.J. Tol of the Economic and Social Research Institute Hamburg, Vrije and Carnegie Mellon Universities immediately published a devastating critique of the Stern Review on 2nd November 2006. He is the author of the UN Handbook on climate change assessment and has worked closely with the IPCC on its three then published reports. He acknowledged that it could not be said that climate change was not a problem and confirmed that he believed that greenhouse gasses should be reduced. However Dr Tol condemned the *"now and forever"* finding as *"preposterous"*. He attacked the Review's selection bias for not being random, having its emphasis on the most pessimistic studies, and made it clear that, although the Review claimed that a cost-benefit analysis was done, none was actually carried out. Dr Tol concluded that the Stern Review should be dismissed as *"alarmist and incompetent"*.

The Stern Review has also been severely attacked for distorting IPCC statements and data, ignoring caveats and statements of advised caution in IPCC reports, not attempting an evaluation of scientific research tending to opinions contrary to its assessments and for its grotesquely selective use of data whilst ignoring key data altogether.[38] Nor does the Review contain any discussion of the scientific destruction of Mann's hockey stick.

Mr Blair's tipping points: leading the EU on climate change

It is now clear that the Stern Review was intended to provide Mr Blair with the script for the role he assumed for himself in Europe as its leading political figure in the fight against climate change. In his Open Letter to EU leaders of February 2006 he had told them that *"We have a window of only 10 to 15 years to take the steps we need to avoid crossing catastrophic tipping points"*. This is, and was intended to be, a terrifying threat to mankind.

It must, however, be understood that there is no scientific justification for such a statement. In the extent to which it misleads, this statement of Mr Blair ranks as low as the discredited statements as to WMD in Saddam's Iraq. Even at times in the planet's history when atmospheric concentrations were 25 times higher than today there were no runaway greenhouse effect or tipping points".[39] The first 20ppmv of

---

38   Plimer, *op. cit.*, pages 476 – 479

39   Plimer, *op. cit.*, pages 375, 402, 488

CO2 has the greatest effect on temperature. At 200ppmv CO2 utility in absorbing infra – red energy is almost exhausted. At the existing levels of 385ppmv further concentrations will have little effect on back radiation".[40]

This was followed by the Government commissioned Stern Report in October 2006, and Mr Blair's Downing Street reception in January 2007 for Global Cool whose celebrities include Leonardo Di Caprio, Orlando Bloom and Jude Law with its slogan of "Ten Years to Save the Planet" which in turn heralded the publication of the 2007 IPPC report the following month.

The EU Green Paper in June 2007 and the Communication of the EU Commission Europe's Climate Change Opportunity (COM/2008/final) in January 2008 are the backdrop to the showpiece of the UK government's climate change trophies – the Climate Change Act 2008. From 26th November 2008 the Act imposed on the Secretary of State a legal duty to ensure that UK emission of greenhouse gasses were at least 80% lower than the 1990 baseline level. The costs of all this as estimated by Mr Milliband's department of Energy and Climate Change would be £404bn with £18bn being added to electricity bills for every year until 2050. These are truly staggering costs.

The legislation is an indictment of the abject failure of Parliament to apply any serious democratic oversight and scrutiny to a measure that, if fulfilled, would decimate the entire UK economy and deprive it of 40% of its electricity generating capacity.[41] It was passed by 463 votes to 3 with nothing even approaching the degree of scrutiny and investigation that the US Congress had brought to bear on the issue over 20 years.

Since the EU targets, if achieved, would inflict devastation on the major European economies, the citizens of the Member States who are bearing and will have to bear the costs of all this might wish at least to have the comfort of knowing that catastrophic climate change was certain to occur and that the damage it would cause justified severe sacrifices. No such comfort can be gleaned from any action or investigation initiated by the EU. Instead the EU simply relied on the discredited IPCC 2001 report and Stern Review without question. All the scientific criticism of these reports bounced off the Commission's hide, if indeed they were noted at all. It relied expressly on the findings of Stern without question and continues to do so.

---

40   Communication from the Commission to the European Parliament – 20 20 by 2020 –Europe's
     climate change opportunity. COM(2008)13 final. 23.01.2008

41   Booker C. The Real Global Warming Disaster, 2009, page 283 published by Continuum
     International Publishing Group

Now however the EU had to consider the 2007 IPCC fourth report in the context of its new 20:20:20 policies.

2007 IPCC Report: 2009 White Paper

The 2007 IPCC Report Summary for Policy Makers was published in February 2007. The key section on Climate Change Predictions was the work of just 12 authors who relied on 78 contributors. It became the object of a wave of scientific dissent reflected in the publication of the opinions of over 700 scientists set out in the Senate Minority Report already referred to.

It asserted that *"Warming of the climate system is now unequivocal"*. It also asserted that the *"incidence of extreme high sea level has increased world wide"*. It claimed that there was now evidence of the melting of Himalyan glaciers due to human emissions of greenhouse gasses. The IPCC has now acknowledged (20th January 2010) that these claims are unfounded. The report on which this claim depended was not peer-reviewed scientific literature but simply a media interview with a scientist conducted in 1999. Several senior scientists have now confirmed that the claim was untenable.

However in many key respects its conclusions were much more tentative and cautious than the 2001 report. In particular its forecast of global temperature rise was much more modest *"this is likely to lie in the range 2°C to 4.5°C, with a most likely value of about 3°C...For fundamental physical reasons, as well as data limitations, values substantially higher than 4.5°C still cannot be excluded"*. Again its predictions on sea level rise by 2100 were scaled down severely (18cm – 59 cm) and much greater uncertainty was acknowledged with the IPCC explaining that its prediction scenarios had *"5 to 95% ranges based on the spread of Atmosphere Ocean General Circulation Models results, not including uncertainty in carbon cycle feedbacks"*. The report accepted the indicated *"uncertainty in global warming due to future changes in the carbon cycle"*.

This uncertainty reflects the fact that as has been shown, the evidence does not point to certain and unequivocal conclusions. There is no certainty that rising sea levels are abnormally occurring much less that they are caused by human induced global warming. Indeed it is uncertain that sea levels are increasing to any material extent at all. The IPCC's revised average likely temperature rise of 3° was a full 2.8° lower than the 2001 level relied on in the EU's 2005 policy papers. Such an increase would not, as has been shown using the IPCC's own data, have any material impact on global GDP.

None of these uncertainties inform the EU policy documents however. Its 2007 Green Paper repeats without qualification its assertions of the extreme effects of global climate change and relies on the Stern Review. The 2009 White Paper makes no reference to the 2007 IPCC Report but again relies on Stern.

EU 'Consultation'

The EU White Paper asserts that its 2007 Green Paper was *"widely consulted upon"*. However the 'consultation' initiated by the EU is not worthy of the name. The process consisted of a one day conference in Brussels with 17 participants all of whom were active proponents of the EU position on climate change. Others were invited *"to contribute to the debate, including through the use of an internet chat"*.

The conference considered a number of pre-determined questions all of which assume that global warming was settled science and that the serious impacts identified in the Green Paper would occur. The conference opened at 9.00a.m. and closed at 5.30p.m. Regional "workshops" were staged for "European Stakeholders" in Helsinki, Budapest, London and Lisbon. These were 2 day events (except for Budapest – 1 day only). Here again the conclusions of the Green Paper were assumed.

None of this bears any serious consideration – it is a sham and a farce.

The EU Global Warming disaster

Citizens of all Member States might pause to ask if is it really credible that policies involving the devastating transformation of their countries economies should be founded on reports and a Review tainted with such uncertainties and flaws. Yet that is what has happened with the 4 IPCC reports and the Stern Review each of which are the bedrock of such policies as have been imposed since 1990 by the ever extending "competence" of the EU.

The entire EU project on "Climate Change" is an appalling lesson to us all of the dangers that an undemocratised supranational government can inflict on those who are governed by its laws. The measures that the EU is imposing on Europe under the banner of "fighting climate change" will bring disaster on all of the Member States on a scale that utterly overwhelms the follies of the CAP and Common Fisheries Policy - from which at least some Member States derive benefit. It is able to continue on this path without restraint or the arresting effect of informed doubt since it has correctly recognised that public alarm at the proclaimed perils mankind is facing can be turned to account to enlarge, to a decisive extent, its supranational powers and standing. At the same time it is entirely immune to any contrary opinion or expression of popular scepticsm.

It is however some comfort to note the widening impact of the internet and the democratising force that it has become. This has enabled those who are not sure of the evidence to tap into a deepening reservoir of scientific opinion and has given a voice to scientists whose dissent has been suppressed or ridiculed by government and broadcasters. The internet has given rise to world wide dissemination of the opinions of those who hold informed and sincere doubts as the certainties of global warming, its causes, its effects and the options open to mankind. People can in their homes or offices follow the trail of an idea or argument in a way that was simply not posssible 10 years ago. As Professor Hulme has said *"Climate science – like science in general – is being democratised and the IPCC needs to reflect that."*

Mounting disquiet with the IPCC Process

Before examining the approach adopted by the US Congress to the phenomenon of supposed global warming it must be understood that the entire IPCC process is now being called into question. There is a serious risk that it will become so discredited as to deprive it of any validity. Not only has the entire Mann 'hockey stick' farce exposed it to the ridicule of sceptical observers but, more gravely, disturbing evidence has very recently emerged of shocking unprofessional conduct in one of the four institutions used as a key source in the compiling of IPCC reports.

The exposure of the Mann "hockey stick" as a seriously flawed document – one which its author was aware had no statistical validity – in the hearings before the US Congress Committees in 2005 and 2006 sent a shock wave throughout scientific community concerned with global warming. So dubious were Mann's methods that they have given rise to calls from respected scientists for him to be barred from all further participation in the IPCC.

Yet the discrediting of Mann was given no weight at all by the UK's Met Office's Hadley Centre Climate Research Unit (CRU) in the University of East Anglia. Since the CRU is one of the four centres providing temperature date on which the IPCC relies in its reports it would not have been surprising if its scientists had disassociated themselves wholly from Mann and his discredited work - not least because he had simply 'eliminated' the earlier Mediaeval Warming period and the Little Ice Age in order to produce a flat line with an explosive temperature rise in the last 20 years.

So far from this being the case Professor Philip Jones advised Mann that if there was a chance of the true data being revealed to the outside world he would delete the key file rather than reveal it. He refused to release basic data from which the CRU had produced its highly influential temperature record and proposed means by which disclosure could be frustrated.

It is barely credible to recount that in 2008, immediately after the CRU received a request by David Holland under the Freedom of Information Act to produce the key data, Jones sent an e-mail to Mann asking him to arrange to delete e-mail traffic between a number of fellow IPCC contributors which bore directly on the information the CRU was bound by law to produce. All this was done to prevent it emerging that data had been cynically manipulated in order to produce the impression of violently accelerated warming.

Once the CRU was compelled to produce the data it then emerged that not only was there a conspiracy to conceal data but also that the entire 'peer review' process by which climate change scientific papers were scrutinised anonymously by others had been corrupted. This peer review procedure had already been condemned by a report to the Energy and Commerce Committee of the House of Representatives of US Congress in 2006, as will be seen later in this paper. So debased was the system of review that in March 2004 Professor Jones wrote to Mann commenting that he had rejected two papers showing the defective quality of temperature data from Siberian weather locations - which had been used by the CRU to show exceptional warming in the 20th century - and that he [Jones] *"had gone to town in both reviews.... If either appears I would be very surprised"*. Later that year, confronted by two learned papers published in 'Climate Research', Jones told Mann that he could not *"see either of these papers being in the next IPCC report. ....I will keep them out somehow – even if we have to redefine what peer review literature is"*

Now, to add to the mounting disquiet as to the bias and presumption shown by the CRU, a key member of the independent panel formed to investigate all of this has had to resign. The editor in chief of Nature, Phillip Campbell, holds a highly regarded and important position – his publication is one of the most renowned in the scientific world. However it is also known for its publication of significant papers supporting the flawed 'hockey stick' graph. On 11th February 2010, almost immediately after the panel was set up, he was compelled to resign on the grounds of clear perceived bias.

Congress and Global Warming

Nowhere are the effects of the democratic process on the unfolding concern as to global warming better seen than in the USA. At every stage of this story the houses of the US Congress have exercised the power that is invested in them by the US democracy itself to enquire into the validity or otherwise of the key claims made in the Global Warming debate. This is something that deserves our respect and gratitude and it is with a brief examination of how global warming has fared in the democracy of the Great Republic that this paper concludes.

The world wide alarm on global warming was set off by the evidence given on 23rd June 1988 by James Hansen before a hearing before the US Senate Committee on Energy and Natural Resources. The Committee was holding hearings as part of its investigation into the greenhouse effect and global warming. It is telling that the very origins of global warming as cause for concern lie at the heart of US democracy.

During the 20 years since that Committee hearing the US Congress has conducted or initiated an extraordinary number of investigations into the existence of global warming, its causes and effects and options for addressing it. These hearings involve taking sworn evidence from all sides of the debate and from witnesses who are leading acknowledged experts in their fields. These are extremely thorough and far reaching investigations and have a decisive effect on the path of proposed legislation.

Indeed the more alarmist and the more sceptical Congressman are known US national figures in the US. Senator Gore, of course, is known world wide but Senator James Inhofe the ranking Minority Member of the Senate Committee on Environment and Public Works is also celebrated for his persistent challenge to the assumed certainties of the science.

The US electorate has been an important component in this democratic oversight. Climate change was a key election issue in the 2008 Obama/McCain presidential campaign and the cost of the American Clean Air and Security Bill passed by just 219 votes to 212 by the House of Representatives - now to navigate the Senate - is of deep concern to the US electorate – a sensitivity to the burden of tax revealed again in January 2010 in the shock victory of Scott P. Brown in the Massachusetts Senate election.

At least 3 Senate Committees have conducted such investigations and 2 Committees of the House of Representatives. To have a notion of the scale and depth of these Congressional hearings it is well worth the effort of undertaking an internet review of the Senate and House Committee hearings on an extraordinary range of aspects of the global warming issue and to download or in, some cases, listen to the key evidence.

7 Days in 2007

Take just one week in February 2007. On 7 February 2007 the Senate Committee on Commerce Science and Transportation held a hearing on *Climate Change and Scientific Enquiry*. The Majority Leader, Senator Inouye, in his opening statement set out the much larger role of Congress in determining the scientific basis of its decisions;

> *"We in Congress as well as decision makers within the regulatory agencies must examine and weigh the scientific evidence to guide changes in policies, laws, and regulations. To make the best decisions, we need free access to unbiased scientific findings and conclusions because the quality of our decisions is highly dependent upon the science we use to make those decisions."*

On 13 February 2007 the Senate Committee on Energy and Natural Resources held a hearing on the *Stern Review on the Economics of Climate Change* to examine the economic impacts of climate change calling the author of the Stern Review and other expert witnesses from MIT and Wesleyan University to give detailed evidence on the validity of the assessments given in the Review.

14 days in 2010

Or consider just the 2 weeks to 4 February 2010. The Senate Committee on Energy and Natural Resources hearing opened on 21 January 2010 on the *"Research, development, priorities and imperatives needed to meet the medium and long term challenges associated with climate change"*. This followed the hearing of the Committee opened on 2 December 2009 to receive testimony on *"Policy options for reducing greenhouse gas emissions"*. Meanwhile the Senate Committee on Environment and Public Works opened its hearing on Green Jobs and the New Economy: Solar Energy Technology and Clean Energy Jobs on 28 January 2010. The House Committee on Science and Technology hearing on *"Geotechnoloy: The Scientific Basis and Engineering Challenges"* opened on 4 February 2010.

Given the wide extent of this democratic oversight it is only possible to look more closely at 2 of the key Congressional hearings on the IPCC reports themselves.

Senate Commerce and Science Committee May 2001
The Summary for Policy Makers under the 2001 IPCC Report was much criticised on the grounds that it was prepared by a small number of authors – not more than 14 in number – who had drastically simplified the text in the original of the draft Summary to remove the uncertainties that the full text had still retained.

It was the sworn testimony given before a hearing of the Senate Commerce and Science Committee on 1st May 2001 that revealed this state of affairs. Dr Richard Lindzen, Professor of Meteorology at the Massachusetts Institute of Technology, testified at length with detailed scientific data as to the flawed methodology of the IPCC reporting process and its over reliance on computer models. He was a lead author of Chapter 7, 'Physical Climate Processes and Feedbacks,' of the 2001 report and had protested about the distortions contained in the Summary for Policy Makers. Referring to the supposed 'consensus' his evidence included the following statements:

"In truth, neither the full text of the IPCC documents nor even the summaries claim any such agreement. Claiming the agreement of thousands of scientists is certainly easier than trying to understand the issue or to respond to scientific questions; it also effectively intimidates most citizens. However, the invocation of the IPCC is more a mantra than a proper reflection on that flawed document".

There is no doubt that this testimony added to the growing scepticsm in the US which underlay the decision earlier that year by its decision not to ratify the Kyoto Protocol.

House Committees: Energy and Commerce:
Science and Technology: 2005/2006.
Included in some of the most influential and important hearings were those of the House Committees on Energy and Commerce and (separately) on Science and Technology in 2005 and 2006. These hearings arose out of the investigations of the IPCC findings in its 2001 report and the refusal of Mr Mann to produce to the Energy and Commerce Committee the computer codes that he had used to generate the hockey stick graph on which the IPCC report so much relied and which had caused such alarm. As a consequence of this the Commerce Committee held hearings to determine the basis for the hockey stick graph. Meanwhile the House Science and Technology Committee initiated an investigation by eminent scientists to provide it with expert guidance on the "current scientific consensus" on climate change and on the hockey stick specifically.

The results of these investigations were devastating for the hockey stick graph and the 2001 IPCC report. The report to the Energy Committee established that Mann had misused statistical methods, that his methodology was seriously flawed, that the claim that the 1990's were the hottest decade of the millennium could not be substantiated, that the removal of the Mediaeval Warming and Little Ice Ago could not be justified and that the peer review IPCC process was not independent or impartial. The report found that *"The public policy implications of this debate are financially staggering and yet apparently no independent statistical expertise was sought or used"*.

The Committee made a number of important recommendations including that *"When massive amounts of public monies and human lives are at stake, academic work should have a more intense level of scrutiny and review..."*[42] The report to the Science and Technology Committee was also severely critical of the IPCC report in relation to the hockey stick graph and confirmed that it agreed with the conclusions of the report to the Commerce Committee.

The citizens of the US are part of a great democracy that is robust, active and dominant in the process of government and law making. They are indeed fortunate.

The lesson to be learned

The entire development of the debate in the US has been subjected to exhaustive and wide investigation of every aspect of the climate change concern with the most expert testimony being taken and published on a continuing basis. It is a remarkable example of the power of a sovereign democracy to protect its peoples from imprudent and reckless projects and laws the need for which have not been demonstrated nor whose cost and effectiveness have been exhaustively researched.

No such protection has been conferred on its peoples by the EU. It has betrayed its 'citizens' by inciting serious alarm on this most emotive subject with no regard for the fears, costs and privations its extravagant posturing may cause. The lack of any comparable democratic oversight acting to restrain it and of electoral vindication for its laws and impositions has deprived its policies and directives of all credibility and authority.

---

42   Plimer , *op. cit.* pages 94 and 385

As the Great Republic has demonstrated it is only to a robust and effective democracy that such decisions can be committed. This is indeed the incontrovertible and enduring conclusion of mankind's global warming alarm.

THE BRUGES GROUP | ASSOCIATE MEMBERSHIP

TEL: +44 (0)20 7287 4414 | www.brugesgroup.com/join | info@brugesgroup.com

To join the Bruges Group, complete the following form and send it to the Membership Secretary with your annual subscription fee. This will entitle you to receive our published material for one year. It also helps cover the cost of the numerous Bruges Group meetings to which all Associate Members are invited. **You can also join online, right now, by using your debit or credit card. Please log on to www.brugesgroup.com/join or you can join over the phone by calling 020 7287 4414.**

Minimum Associate Membership Rates for 1 year UK Member £30 ☐ , Europe £45 ☐ , Rest of the world £60 ☐

Optional donation: £10 ☐ £20 ☐ £50 ☐ £100 ☐ £250 ☐ £500 ☐

Other, please specify: ....

If you are able to give more towards our work, we would be very grateful for your support. For the sake of convenience, we urge you to pay by standing order.

YES! I wish to join the Bruges Group

Title: .... Name: ....

Address: ....

.... Postcode: ....

Telephone: ....

Email: ....

BANKERS ORDER Name and full postal address of your Bank or Building Society

To: The Manager:... Bank/Building Society

Address: ....

.... Postcode: ....

Account number: .... Sort code: ....

Please Pay: Barclays Bank Ltd (Sort Code 20-46-73), 6 Clarence St, Kingston-upon-Thames, Surrey KT1 1NY

The sum of £ .... (figures)

Signature: .... Date: ....

to the credit of the Bruges Group A/C No 90211214 forthwith and on the same day in each subsequent year until further notice.

— or —

CHEQUE PAYMENTS I enclose a cheque made payable to the Bruges Group

The sum of £ .... (figures)

Signature: .... Date: ....

— or —

MEMBERSHIP PAYMENT BY CREDIT/DEBIT CARD

Solo ☐ Visa Card ☐ Visa Delta ☐ Visa Electron ☐ Mastercard ☐ JCB ☐ Switch ☐

Card number: ....

Valid from: .... Expiry date: .... Issue number: .... Security code: ....

Card holder's name as it appears on the card (please print): ....

.Address of card holder: ....

.... Postcode: ....

Telephone:...

Email: .... Signature: .... Date: ....

Please complete this form and return to:
The Membership Secretary, The Bruges Group, 227 Linen Hall, 162-168 Regent St., London W1B 5TB

Honorary President: The Rt. Hon the Baroness Thatcher of Kesteven, LG OM FRS
Vice-President: The Rt. Hon the Lord Lamont of Lerwick **Chairman:** Barry Legg
Director: Robert Oulds MA **Head of Research:** Dr Helen Szamuely **Washington D.C. Representative:** John O'Sullivan, CBE
Founder Chairman: Lord Harris of High Cross **Former Chairmen:** Dr Brian Hindley, Dr Martin Holmes & Professor Kenneth Minogue

www.brugesgroup.com